数学帮帮忙 互动版

猫咪城堡

【美】梅尔·弗莱德曼　艾伦·威斯◎著

【美】林·亚当斯◎绘

范晓星◎译

天津出版传媒集团

新蕾出版社

图书在版编目 (CIP) 数据

猫咪城堡/(美)弗莱德曼(Friedman,M.),(美)威斯(Weiss,E.)著;(美)亚当斯
(Adams,L.)绘;范晓星译.
—天津:新蕾出版社,2014.1(2024.12 重印)
(数学帮帮忙·互动版)
书名原文:Kitten Castle
ISBN 978-7-5307-5897-7

Ⅰ.①猫…
Ⅱ.①弗…②威…③亚…④范…
Ⅲ.①数学–儿童读物
Ⅳ.①O1–49

中国版本图书馆 CIP 数据核字(2013)第 270444 号

Kitten Castle by Mel Friedman/Ellen Weiss;
Illustrated by Lynn Adams.
Copyright ⓒ 2001 by Kane Press, Inc.
All rights reserved, including the right of reproduction in whole or in part in any
form. This edition published by arrangement with Kane Press, Inc. New York, NY,
represented by Lerner Publishing Group through The ChoiceMaker Korea Co.
Agency.
Simplified Chinese translation copyright ⓒ 2014 by New Buds Publishing House
(Tianjin) Limited Company
ALL RIGHTS RESERVED
本书中文简体版专有出版权经由中华版权代理中心授予新蕾出版社(天津)有
限公司。未经许可,不得以任何方式复制或抄袭本书的任何部分。
津图登字:02-2012-225

出版发行:天津出版传媒集团
新蕾出版社
http://www.newbuds.com.cn
地　　址:天津市和平区西康路 35 号(300051)
出 版 人:马玉秀
电　　话:总编办 (022)23332422
发行部 (022)23332679　23332351
传　　真:(022)23332422
经　　销:全国新华书店
印　　刷:天津新华印务有限公司
开　　本:787mm×1092mm　1/16
印　　张:3
版　　次:2014 年 1 月第 1 版　2024 年 12 月第 24 次印刷
定　　价:12.00 元

无处不在的数学

资深编辑 卢 江

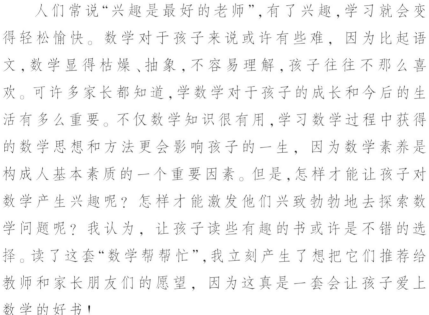

　　人们常说"兴趣是最好的老师",有了兴趣,学习就会变得轻松愉快。数学对于孩子来说或许有些难,因为比起语文,数学显得枯燥、抽象,不容易理解,孩子往往不那么喜欢。可许多家长都知道,学数学对于孩子的成长和今后的生活有多么重要。不仅数学知识很有用,学习数学过程中获得的数学思想和方法更会影响孩子的一生,因为数学素养是构成人基本素质的一个重要因素。但是,怎样才能让孩子对数学产生兴趣呢? 怎样才能激发他们兴致勃勃地去探索数学问题呢? 我认为,让孩子读些有趣的书或许是不错的选择。读了这套"数学帮帮忙",我立刻产生了想把它们推荐给教师和家长朋友们的愿望,因为这真是一套会让孩子爱上数学的好书!

　　这套有趣的图书从美国引进,原出版者是美国资深教育专家。每本书讲述一个孩子们生活中的故事,由故事中出现的问题自然地引入一个数学知识,然后通过运用数学知识解决问题。比如,从帮助外婆整理散落的纽扣引出分类,从为小狗记录藏骨头的地点引出空间方位等等。故事素材全部来源于孩子们的真实生活，不是童话，不是幻想，而是鲜活的生活实例。正是这些发生在孩子身边的故事，让孩子们懂得，数学无处不在并且非常有用；这些鲜活的实例也使得抽象的概念更易于理解，更容易激发孩子学习数学的兴趣，让他们逐渐爱上数学。这样的教育思想和方法与我国近年来提倡的数学教育理念是十分吻合的！

这是一套适合5~8岁孩子阅读的书，书中的有趣情节和生动的插画可以将抽象的数学问题直观化、形象化，为孩子的思维活动提供具体形象的支持。如果亲子共读的话，家长可以带领孩子推测情节的发展，探讨解决难题的办法，让孩子在愉悦的氛围中学到知识和方法。

值得教师和家长朋友们注意的是，在每本书的后面，出版者还加入了"互动课堂"及"互动练习"，一方面通过一些精心设计的活动让孩子巩固新学到的数学知识，进一步体会知识的含义和实际应用；另一方面帮助家长指导孩子阅读，体会故事中数学之外的道理，逐步提升孩子的阅读理解能力。

我相信孩子读过这套书后一定会明白，原来，数学不是烦恼，不是包袱，数学真能帮大忙！

　　星期六早晨的足球训练过后,安娜一口气跑回家。

　　"有了吗?"她张口就问妈妈。

　　"你自己去看吧。"科尔太太微笑着说道。

安娜冲进小书房。就在那儿，她们家的猫咪花纹儿躺在角落里。在她身边，依偎着四只刚出生的小猫咪。

"生日快乐，小猫咪！"安娜说。

　　吃晚饭的时候，安娜问了爸爸妈妈一个很重要的
问题："我们能把小猫都留下吗？"

　　"也许行吧。"科尔太太说。

　　"也许不行。"科尔先生说，"我们已经有五条小金
鱼、两只仓鼠、一只金丝雀，再加上花纹儿。九只宠物难
道还不够吗？"

"哦,爸爸,求求您了!"安娜央求道,"我会好好儿照顾他们的。"

科尔先生想了一会儿。"好吧。"他慢慢地说道,"他们可以留下,只要不碍事就行。"

　　小猫咪一天天变得可爱起来。一只小猫有着巧克力色的皮毛,安娜叫她小糖豆。小糖豆很可爱,她喜欢在有弧度的地方蜷成一团,不喜欢有棱有角的地方。

另一只小猫是个登高能手。他喜欢爬到安娜的玩具箱上,坐在箱子边。等其他小猫经过的时候,他就冷不丁扑上去!

"他就叫小埋伏。"安娜宣布。

"我看他是个很讨厌的家伙。"科尔先生说。

埃及

穿靴子的猫

第三只小猫长得最可爱。安娜决定叫她小可爱。

小可爱对她的玩具很挑剔。她只喜欢玩能滚来滚去的东西。于是安娜给了她三样可以滚的玩具。

　　第四只小猫喜欢在屋子里东窜西窜，把东西弄翻。他会消失几个小时，然后从最奇怪的地方突然现身。

　　"这只小猫可真是个麻烦。"科尔先生说。小麻烦就这样有了自己的名字。

一天早上，小埋伏跳到科尔先生的胸口上，把他弄醒了。

然后，小糖豆想窝在科尔先生的废纸篓里，却把纸篓弄翻了。

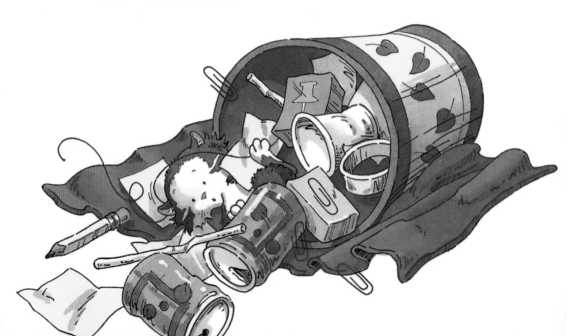

紧接着，小可爱发现了一件可以滚的新玩具——科尔先生最心爱的钢笔。

小麻烦呢？他钻进科尔先生的衣橱里，把他所有的领带都扯了下来，然后在一只鞋子里睡着了。

"就这么决定了。"科尔先生说,"必须把这些小猫送走!"

"再给他们一次机会吧。"安娜央求道。

科尔先生叹了口气。"好吧。"他说,"明天我要出差。等我回来咱们再做决定。"

　　第二天，安娜给她最好的朋友汤姆打电话。
"快点过来！"她说，"你一定要帮我留下这几只
猫咪。"安娜把遇到的问题都告诉了汤姆。

汤姆马上就到了。"好吧。"他说,"你爸爸并不介意其他宠物,对吧?"

　　"他们从来不给他添乱。"安娜说,"仓鼠在笼子里,金鱼在鱼缸里……"

　　"说的就是!"汤姆说,"我们得给小猫咪做个他们自己的窝!"

穿靴子的

"当然啦。"安娜说,"我们可以利用盒子,在里面放上一大堆猫咪们喜欢的东西。"

"我们还可以把窝造得很漂亮。"汤姆说。

安娜指向一本故事书说:"就像一座城堡!"

　　"我们需要盒子、胶带、细绳……"汤姆说。

　　"还有颜料和记号笔。"安娜说，"咱们先在房间里找材料吧！"

　　他们一直忙到吃晚饭的时候。

第二天早上，汤姆起床第一件事就是赶到安娜家。

"我们给每只小猫都量身打造一间小屋吧。"安娜说。

小可爱的房子是第一个造好的。他们把这间小屋造得非常可爱，色调明快，还有一座别致的小吊桥。但小可爱怎么也不肯进去。

　　安娜有了个主意。她把小可爱能滚的玩具都放了进去。"现在这里就是她真正的家了。"她说。

　　小可爱也是这么想的。她跑进小屋，玩起了自己的小漏斗。

下一个是小糖豆的房间。安娜和汤姆在小可爱的房间旁边放了一个大盒子，还涂上了颜色。可他们刚把小糖豆抱进去，她马上就跳了出来。

"我敢说是因为这里面太四四方方了。"安娜说。

"啊？"汤姆说。

　　"小糖豆喜欢有弧度的地方。"安娜解释道,"她不喜欢四四方方、有棱有角的地方。"

　　"嗯,那个帽盒怎么样?"汤姆问,"它是圆形的。"

　　于是,他们换了一个新盒子。小糖豆马上跳进去蜷缩起来。"甜蜜的新家二号。"安娜说。

转天是星期五,科尔先生星期六就要回来了!

"我们要赶快把小埋伏的房间造好。"安娜说,"他需要一个很高的盒子,这样他能从上面跳下来。"

他们把手里最高的盒子摞在小糖豆的新家上面。小埋伏跳来跳去,仿佛来到了开心乐园。

"就差一个房间了。"安娜说。

"小麻烦会喜欢什么样的房间?"汤姆问,"有弧度的? 四四方方的? 高的? 矮的? "

"谁知道啊!"安娜说,"小麻烦总有新花样!"

他们给小麻烦造了一间漂亮的房子，在二层，里面还有一只玩具小老鼠。"小猫咪都喜欢玩具老鼠。"安娜说。

他们又拿了很多猫咪玩具和午睡用的小靠垫。他们还给新房子加了高塔、尖顶和旗子。这座猫咪城堡看起来棒极了！

"来吧，小猫咪！"安娜说，"我们做好啦！"

所有的小猫咪都来了，只有小麻烦不见了。

安娜和汤姆呼唤着小麻烦的名字。
他们找啊找。
他们拿了小麻烦爱吃的东西。
可小麻烦就是不肯露面。

周六上午,安娜的爸爸回到家里。小麻烦还没有找到。可科尔先生只注意到家里很安静,很整洁。

"发生什么事了?"他说,"灯没有倒,脚边也没有小猫绊脚。"

"爸爸,跟我们来吧。"安娜说。

安娜和汤姆带着科尔先生来到小书房。

"安娜！"科尔先生说，"这真不错啊！"

"这是一座城堡。"汤姆说。

"一座猫咪城堡。"安娜说。

"小麻烦在哪儿？"科尔先生问。

"我们找不到他了。"安娜说。

突然，他们听到从门厅的壁橱里传来一些响动，和一声小小的猫叫。安娜打开门，"小麻烦！"她喊道，"原来你在这里！"

科尔先生哈哈大笑起来："原来那只旧鞋在这里啊！也许这才是小麻烦的家。"

"您的意思是，我们可以留下这些小猫了？"安娜问。

"是的。"科尔先生微笑着说。

于是，小麻烦和他的鞋子一起搬进了猫咪城堡。

打那以后，小麻烦再也不惹麻烦了，至少在他睡觉的时候！

立体图形

下面是一些用来描述形状的词语:

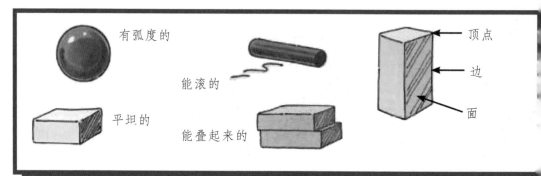

形状	有弧度还是平坦的?	能滚还是能叠起来的?	几个面?	几个顶点?	几条边?
长方体	平坦	可以叠起来	6	8	12
正方体	平坦	可以叠起来	6	8	12

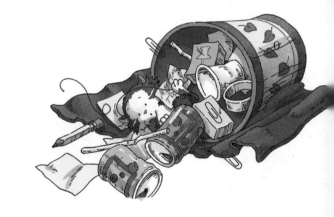

亲爱的家长朋友,请您和孩子一起完成下面这些内容,会有更大的收获哟!

提高阅读能力

• 看看封面和书名,和孩子讨论一下城堡和普通的房子有什么不同?请孩子猜想一下,猫咪城堡会是什么样子?

• 读完故事后,请孩子描述每只猫的样子。在每张插图中,这些小猫都在做什么?

• 请孩子注意故事中描述形状的词语。第 4 页中,花纹儿在角落里是什么姿势?第 22 页中,有弧度的帽盒是什么形状的?

巩固数学概念

- 给孩子准备一些立体图形,如球体(可以用皮球),长方体(可以用盒子),圆柱体(用罐头)。看看插图,还有什么东西能用上。请孩子研究每种图形的特点,哪些会滚?哪些可以叠起来?哪些是平坦的?哪些有弧度?

- 用第 32 页上的图表复习下列词语:有弧度的,平坦的,能滚的,能叠起来的,顶点,面,边。请孩子用这些词语来描述日常用品。

- 拿出一个大盒子和一个小盒子,请孩子比较一下它们的面数一样多吗?想一想利用盒子或者积木的面,我们可以做些什么呢?

生活中的数学

- 帮孩子把土豆切成小小的正方体,让孩子数一数土豆块有几个面,几个顶点,几条边?把孩子的计算结果和第 32 页上的表格进行比较。

- 请孩子想象自己在一个正方体或球体里面。请孩子画幅图,或者描述一下他在里面的感觉。

安娜给我出了一些图形谜题，从下面右边的 2 个图形中找出正确的,画上"○"。

方方正正的		

有 2 个圆面的		

能滚动的		

摸一摸有 8 个角的		

能够四处滚动的		

应该圈什么颜色?

把怎么看都是圆的、可以到处滚动的物品,用红色圈起来。

把可以滚动、也可以立起来的物品用蓝色圈起来。

把 6 个面都是正方形的用绿色圈起来。

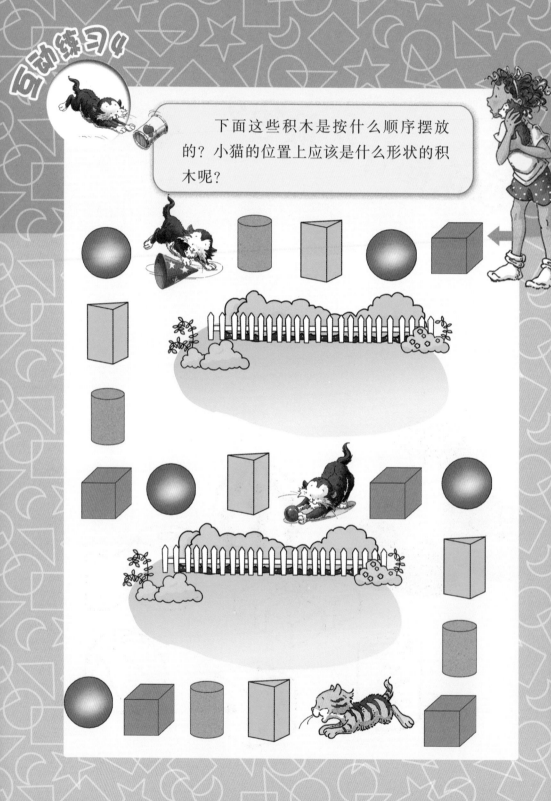

下面这些积木是按什么顺序摆放的？小猫的位置上应该是什么形状的积木呢？

这是汤姆搭的积木,每一组都有 2 种积木没有用上。找一找,圈出来。

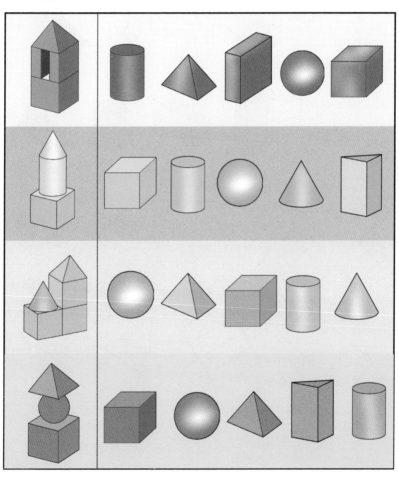

折纸的乐趣

下面的每张纸都能折成1种立体图形，请你仔细观察，根据折痕，想一想，连一连。

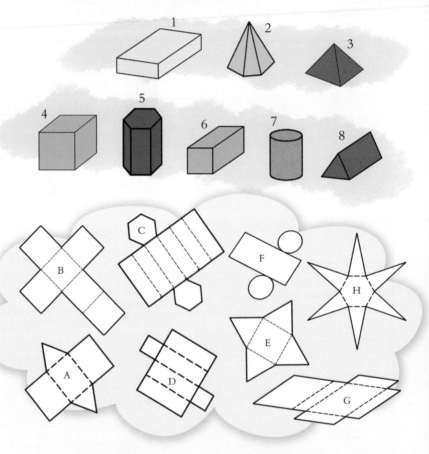

后面也附了一些折纸游戏，你可以剪下来，折一折，把它们变成自己的收藏品。

附页：

参考答案

互动练习1：

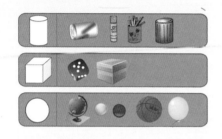

互动练习2：

方方正正的

有2个圆面的

能滚动的

摸一摸有8个角的

能够四处滚动的

互动练习3：

互动练习4：

互动练习5：

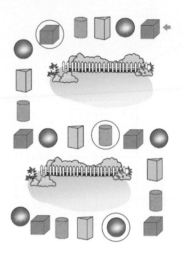

互动练习6：

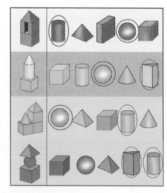

1.G 2.H 3.E
4.B 5.C 6.D
7.F 8.A

互动练习7：略

（习题设计：李　郦）

Kitten Castle

Anna raced home after soccer practice on Saturday morning.

"Did it happen?" she asked her mom.

"See for yourself," Mrs. Cole said with a grin.

Anna dashed into the den. There, off in a corner, lay Streaks, the family cat. And nestled beside her were four tiny new kittens.

"Happy Birthday, kitties!" Anna said.

At dinner, Anna asked her parents the Big Question. "Can we keep the kittens?"

"Maybe," said Mrs. Cole.

"Maybe not," said Mr. Cole. "We have five goldfish, two hamsters, one canary—plus Streaks. Aren't nine pets enough?"

"Oh, pleeease, Daddy," Anna begged. "I'll take good care of them."

Mr. Cole thought for a while. "Okay," he said slowly. "They can stay. But only if they don't get in the way."

The kittens grew cuter every day. One had a chocolate coat. Anna named her Fudge. She was a cuddly kitten who liked to curl up in curvy places. Fudge hated corners.

Another kitten was a big climber. He liked to scramble up onto Anna's toy chest and sit at the edge. When the other kittens went by, he'd pounce!

43

"He's Ambush," Anna declared.

"He's a big pain," Mr. Cole said.

The third kitten had the sweetest face. Anna decided to call her Lovely.

Lovely was fussy about her toys. She only liked to play with things that rolled. So Anna gave her three roly toys.

The fourth kitten liked to tear around the house knocking things over. He'd disappear for hours, then turn up in the oddest places.

"That kitten is trouble," Mr. Cole said. And that's how Trouble got his name.

One morning Ambush woke Mr. Cole by jumping on his chest.

Then Fudge tried to curl up in Mr. Cole's wastebasket and knocked it over.

Next, Lovely found a new toy that rolled—Mr. Cole's favorite pen.

And Trouble? He slipped into Mr. Cole's closet and pulled down all his ties. Then he fell asleep in a shoe.

"That's it," said Mr. Cole. "These kittens must go!"

"Give them just one more chance," Anna begged.

Mr. Cole sighed. "Okay," he said. "I go away on business tomorrow. We'll decide when I get back."

The next day Anna phoned her best friend, Tom. "Come over quick!" she said. "You've got to help me save the kittens." Then she told him all about her problem.

Tom came right over. "Okay," he said. "Your dad doesn't mind the other pets, right?"

"They never bother him," Anna said. "The hamster stays in his cage. The goldfish is in his bowl..."

"Exactly!" Tom said. "We need to make the kittens a place of their own!"

"Of course," Anna said. "We can use boxes and put in lots of things the kittens will like."

"We can make it look cool, too," Tom said.

Anna pointed at a storybook. "Like a castle!" she said.

"We'll need boxes, tape, string..." Tom said.

"And paint and markers," said Anna. "Let's search the house!"

They kept on going until suppertime.

Tom was at Anna's first thing in the morning.

"Let's give each kitten its own special room," said Anna.

Lovely's box was first. They made it extra lovely, with bright colors and a fancy drawbridge. But Lovely wouldn't go in.

Anna had an idea. She put Lovely's roly toys inside. "Now it's really her home," she said.

Lovely thought so, too. She ran inside and started rolling her funnel.

Fudge's room was next. Anna and Tom put a large box next to Lovely's and painted it. But when they put Fudge inside, she jumped right out.

"I'll bet it's too boxy," Anna said.

"Huh?" said Tom.

"Fudge likes curvy places," explained Anna. "Not square ones with corners."

"Well, how about that hatbox?" Tom said. "It's round."

So they switched boxes. Right away, Fudge hopped in and curled up. "Home sweet home number two," Anna said.

The next day was Friday. Mr. Cole would be back Saturday!

"We'd better hurry and do Ambush's room," Anna said. "He needs a tall box so he can jump off it."

They stacked their tallest box on top of Fudge's. Ambush was in pounce heaven.

"One room to go," said Anna.

"What kind of room would Trouble like?" asked Tom. "Curvy? Square? High? Low?"

"Who knows?" Anna said. "Trouble is full of surprises."

They gave Trouble a nice room on the second floor with a toy mouse inside. "All the kittens like toy mice," Anna said.

They put in more cat toys and little pillows for naps. They added towers, pointy tops, and flags. The castle looked amazing!

"Here, kittens!" called Anna. "We're done!"

All the kittens came—except Trouble.

Anna and Tom called Trouble.

They looked for Trouble.

They put snacks out for Trouble.

But Trouble didn't come.

Anna's father got home Saturday morning. Trouble was still missing. But all Mr. Cole noticed was the peace and quiet.

"What happened?" he said. "There are no lamps crashing or kittens underfoot."

"Just follow us, Daddy," Anna said.

Anna and Tom led Mr. Cole into the den.

"Anna!" Mr. Cole said. "This is great!"

"It's a castle," said Tom.

"A Kitten Castle," said Anna.

"Where's Trouble?" Mr. Cole asked.

"We can't find him," said Anna.

All of a sudden they heard a noise coming from the hall closet. A little mewing noise. Anna opened the door. "Trouble!" she said. "There you are!"

Mr. Cole started to laugh. "So that's where that old shoe was. Maybe it should be Trouble's."

"You mean, we can keep the kittens?" Anna asked.

"Yes," said Mr. Cole with a big grin.

And so, Trouble—and his shoe—moved into the Kitten Castle.

After that, Trouble wasn't trouble anymore—at least not when he was sleeping!